introduction

Comfort food, a starter, a quick lunch on the go or food for the soul – soup is a brilliantly versatile meal and, as these 60 delicious recipes will show you, it's a Food Optimiser's best friend!

Packed with healthy, tasty and filling Free and Superfree Foods, Slimming World's *Little Book of Soups* features hearty winter warmers, traditional family favourites, elegant recipes ideal for entertaining and refreshing chilled soups – perfect for the summer months.

Most of the recipes are Free on Extra Easy and, in true Food Optimising style, they're extra easy on your pocket too. Many can be prepared in advance and frozen, making them the perfect 'ready meal' – and with a little help from your store cupboard staples you can transform basic, inexpensive, everyday ingredients into delicious meals that the whole family will enjoy.

Symbol sense

The Syn values for each recipe are
included in these coloured hearts.
Take a look at the orange heart for
Extra Easy, the green heart for the
Green choice and the red heart for the
Original choice. If a recipe's Free you'll
see an 'F' inside, and if it contains
Syns you'll see the value per serving.

We've marked vegetarian
recipes with *Ⓥ*.

souper tips

The soup-maker's store cupboard

The best thing about making soup is that you can use just about any ingredient. Leftover veg from Sunday lunch, the swede you never got around to using – even the lettuce that never made it to the salad bowl. However, there are a few soup staples that will make your life easier if you keep them in your store cupboard. Lentils are great for adding body to your soup base. Tinned pulses such as cannellini beans, chickpeas and kidney beans add texture and substance to soup – and fill you up too! Tinned tomatoes and passata are also a useful standby. Herbs and spices are essential – fresh herbs are always better if you can get them, however, some dried herbs work well, such as rosemary, thyme and bay leaves.

Fresh chopped herbs can be frozen in ice cubes and added to soups while cooking.

A good soup base

A good stock is at the heart of a good soup! Most people nowadays simply don't have time to simmer a vegetable, chicken or meat stock for several hours, though if you have the time, it does produce a more flavoursome base. The good news for busy cooks is that stock cubes, bouillon powder, stock concentrate and ready-to-use liquid stocks are all Free when you're Food Optimising.

Through thick or thin

For a smooth textured soup, we recommend you use a blender or food processor – avoid overfilling it and make sure the soup has cooled before puréeing. For speed and to save on washing up, invest in a stick blender – you literally stick it in your saucepan of soup, tilt the pan slightly and whizz to a smooth purée. For a thicker textured soup, purée cooked red lentils, potatoes or swede and add to give the desired thickness. For a quick-fix thickener, remove a ladleful of soup, purée and add back to the main soup.

Freezing soups

Most of the soups in this book can be made in advance and frozen – you'll find a ❄ symbol next to freezer-friendly recipes. Allow the soup to cool completely before decanting into freezerproof containers. Seal, label and freeze vegetable soups for up to 4 months, meat and poultry soups for up to 3 months and fish soups for up to 1 month. Vegetable soups can be reheated gently from frozen, adding a splash of water to prevent burning. Meat, fish and poultry soups should be defrosted thoroughly before reheating gently.

light
& fresh

nice
& spicy

a **meal**
in a **bowl**

rich
&smooth

light & fresh

You'll love these deliciously light consommés and chilled soups, which use fresh Free foods to create simple refreshing flavours.

500g large plum or vine tomatoes, skinned and chopped

1 green pepper, deseeded and roughly chopped

1 small cucumber, peeled and roughly chopped

3 spring onions, trimmed and chopped

1 small red chilli, deseeded and finely chopped

2 garlic cloves, peeled and crushed

3 tbsp red wine vinegar

100g fat free natural yogurt

salt and freshly ground black pepper

for the garnish

finely diced tomato, cucumber, red and yellow pepper and red onion

fresh coriander or parsley leaves

fat free natural yogurt

creamy gazpacho

serves 4

takes 25 minutes plus chilling

Place the tomatoes in a food processor along with the pepper, cucumber, spring onions, red chilli, garlic, red wine vinegar, yogurt and 200ml of cold water. Blend until smooth.

Season to taste and pour the blended soup into a large bowl. Cover and chill in the fridge for a minimum of 4 hours before serving.

Serve the gazpacho in chilled bowls or glasses, sprinkled with the assorted garnishes.

Syns per serving 🅕 🅕 🅕

250g frozen baby leaf spinach, defrosted, drained and finely chopped

1 garlic clove, peeled and crushed

1.5cm piece root ginger, peeled and finely grated

500g fat free natural yogurt

salt and freshly ground black pepper

3 tsp dried mint

mint sprigs, to garnish

spinach
& yogurt soup

serves 4 🅥

takes 10 minutes

Place the spinach in a large mixing bowl with the garlic, ginger and yogurt. Season well and stir in the dried mint.

Add 350ml of really cold water and briefly process the mixture in a blender until smooth.

Ladle into chilled bowls with a couple of ice cubes in each, and garnish with mint sprigs.

Syns per serving 🄵 🄵 🄵

vichyssoise

low calorie cooking spray

400g leeks, trimmed
and very finely sliced

200g potatoes, peeled and
cut into small chunks

1 garlic clove, peeled
and crushed

1 bay leaf

800ml vegetable stock

100ml skimmed milk

salt and freshly ground
black pepper

a pinch of freshly
grated nutmeg

4 tbsp snipped fresh
chives plus a few whole
chives, to garnish

fat free natural fromage
frais, to serve

ice cubes, to serve
(if serving chilled)

serves 4
takes 50 minutes

Spray a large non-stick saucepan with low calorie
cooking spray and place over a medium heat. Add the
leeks and potatoes and stir-fry for 3-4 minutes. Add
the garlic, bay leaf and stock and bring to the boil.
Reduce the heat and simmer gently for 20 minutes.
Discard the bay leaf.

Transfer the soup to a food processor and blend until
smooth. Return to the saucepan, pour in the milk and
100ml of water and bring to the boil. Season to taste.
Serve garnished with a pinch of nutmeg, chopped
chives and a swirl of fromage frais.

*This soup is delicious hot or cold.
If you're serving it cold, allow to
cool and then chill in the fridge
for a minimum of 4 hours.
Serve with lots of ice.*

Syns per serving ½ ½ 2½

2 small very ripe
Cantaloupe melons,
about 800g each

1 tsp ground ginger

2 spring onions, trimmed

1 tbsp chopped fresh dill,
plus extra chopped dill
and dill sprigs to garnish

1 tbsp chopped fresh mint

150g fat free natural
yogurt, plus 4 tbsp
to serve

salt and freshly ground
black pepper

chilled melon
& ginger soup

serves 4

takes 20 minutes plus chilling

Cut a thin sliver from the base and top of each melon
so that they will stand upright. Cut in half, scoop out
and discard the seeds.

Holding the melon over a bowl so you don't lose any
lovely juices, use a spoon to scoop out as much flesh
as possible, scraping down the inside of the melon
shell to create a shallow bowl, but leaving enough flesh
on the bottom to keep the bowl from leaking. Place the
melon flesh and juices into a food processor. Add the
ground ginger, spring onions, dill, mint and yogurt and
whizz to a smooth purée. Season to taste and chill the
soup and melon shells for at least 1 hour.

To serve, carefully pour the chilled soup into the melon
shells. Garnish with a swirl of yogurt, a sprinkling of
coarse ground black pepper and chopped dill, plus a
sprig of dill.

Syns per serving 1½ 1½ 1½

1 bunch spring onions, trimmed and finely chopped

2 cucumbers, trimmed, peeled and roughly chopped

1 medium sized potato, peeled and finely chopped

750ml vegetable stock

a small handful fresh mint leaves

150g fat free natural yogurt

salt and freshly ground black pepper

ice cubes, cucumber ribbons and mint sprigs, to garnish

chilled cucumber & mint soup

serves 4-6

takes 40 minutes plus chilling

In a non-stick pan, gently cook the spring onion in four tablespoons of water until softened. Add the cucumber, potato and stock, bring to the boil, cover and simmer for 20-25 minutes.

Allow to cool and then chill the soup completely. Stir in the mint and then blend or whizz in a food processor until smooth. Stir in the yogurt and season to taste.

To serve, place a few ice cubes into a plastic sandwich bag and bash with a rolling pin to crush slightly. Pour the soup into serving bowls and scatter with a few crushed ice cubes and the cucumber ribbons. Garnish with the fresh mint sprigs and serve immediately.

Syns per serving F F 1½

1 onion, peeled and finely chopped

1 garlic clove, peeled and crushed

1 tsp paprika

1 large potato, peeled and finely chopped

400g can chopped tomatoes

juice of ½ lemon

1 bouquet garni

300ml fish or vegetable stock

salt and freshly ground black pepper

175g skinned cod or haddock fillet, cut into small chunks

175g cooked and peeled prawns

fresh flat-leaf parsley, chopped

prawn bisque

serves 4

takes 40 minutes plus chilling

Cook the onion in a non-stick pan with four tablespoons of water for around 3 minutes until softened. Stir in the garlic and simmer for 2-3 minutes or until the water has evaporated.

Add the paprika and cook, stirring for 1 minute. Stir in the potato, chopped tomatoes, lemon juice, bouquet garni and stock. Bring to the boil and simmer for 20 minutes.

Remove the bouquet garni and discard. Whizz the soup base with a stick blender or in a food processor until smooth. Return to the saucepan and heat through gently. Season to taste. Stir in the fish and simmer gently for 5-6 minutes until the fish is cooked through. Stir in the prawns and cook for 1-2 minutes until just heated through. Chill for a minimum of 4 hours and serve scattered with the chopped parsley.

Syns per serving F 4 1½

125g shelled fresh peas

1 small garlic clove

a pinch of coarse salt

2 medium round lettuces
(about 500g in total)
cleaned, torn into pieces
and solid cores discarded

250g fat free natural
yogurt

2cm piece root ginger,
peeled and finely grated

a handful of fresh
mint leaves

juice of ½ lemon

salt and freshly ground
black pepper

lettuce soup
with peas

serves 4 🅥

takes 30 minutes plus chilling

Bring a small amount of water to the boil in a pan, add
the peas and cook for 1 minute. Drain, reserving the
cooking water, cool under cold running water, and
refrigerate. Cut the garlic in half, remove any green at
the centre and discard. Crush the halves with a pinch
of coarse salt.

Combine the garlic with all the other ingredients,
except the peas, in a food processor or blender,
adding just enough of the reserved cooking water to
get the blades moving or until the desired consistency
is achieved – this will vary according to the type of
lettuce and the kind of machine you are using, but you
need to aim to get it fairly smooth.

Season to taste, transfer the soup to a large bowl and
chill for 30 minutes. When ready to serve, stir through
the cooked peas, reserving a few to garnish.

Syns per serving F F 1½

4 large carrots, peeled and roughly chopped

400g beetroot (fresh or vacuum packed), peeled and roughly chopped

3 garlic cloves, peeled and crushed

4 leeks, trimmed and finely sliced

1.2 litres vegetable stock

1 bay leaf

75g fat free natural fromage frais, plus extra to serve

freshly ground black pepper

chopped fresh chives, to garnish

creamed carrot & beetroot soup

serves 4

takes 50 minutes

Place the carrots, beetroot, garlic, leeks, stock and bay leaf in a large saucepan. Cover tightly and cook for 40 minutes, or until the vegetables are tender. Remove the bay leaf and allow to cool slightly.

Transfer the mixture to a food processor. Add the fromage frais and blend until smooth.

Return the soup to the pan and reheat gently.

Sprinkle with freshly ground black pepper, scatter the chives and serve with extra fromage frais.

Syns per serving 🅕 🅕 🅕

low calorie cooking spray

½ small onion, peeled and finely diced

1 garlic clove, peeled and finely diced

750ml chicken stock

60g dried vermicelli or thin noodles

200g cooked skinless and boneless chicken breasts, shredded

4 tbsp chopped fresh flat-leaf parsley

salt and freshly ground black pepper

quick chicken & noodle soup

serves 4

takes 15-20 minutes

Spray a large non-stick frying pan with low calorie cooking spray and place over a medium heat. Add the onion and garlic and gently stir-fry for 1-2 minutes.

Add the stock and vermicelli or noodles and bring to the boil. Cover, reduce the heat to low and cook gently for 6-8 minutes until the vermicelli or noodles are cooked through.

Add the chicken and parsley to the soup and cook for 2-3 minutes until piping hot. Season to taste before serving.

Syns per serving

roasted tomato & basil soup

serves 4

takes 40-45 minutes

2 garlic cloves, peeled and crushed

1 litre hot vegetable stock

salt and freshly ground black pepper

2 tbsp chopped fresh basil, plus extra leaves to garnish

roasted cherry tomatoes, to garnish

Arrange the tomatoes on a baking tray, spray them lightly with low calorie cooking spray and sprinkle with the oregano. Bake in a preheated oven at 200°C/ Fan 180°C/Gas 6 for 10-15 minutes, until the tomatoes start to soften and the skins begin to char.

Meanwhile place the onion and garlic in a large, heavy-based saucepan with 300ml of the stock. Cover the pan, bring to the boil and simmer for 10 minutes.

Peel and chop the roasted tomatoes and add to the cooked onion mixture in the pan along with the remaining stock. Simmer for 15-20 minutes.

Purée the soup in a blender or food processor. Return the soup to the pan, season well and add the basil. Reheat the soup if necessary and serve garnished with some roasted cherry tomatoes and basil leaves.

Syns per serving

1 onion, peeled and finely chopped

2 celery sticks, finely chopped

2 garlic cloves, peeled and finely chopped

600g frozen peas

1 litre vegetable stock

6 tbsp very finely chopped fresh mint

fat free natural yogurt, to serve

freshly ground black pepper

pea & mint soup

serves 4 ❋ *V*

takes 40 minutes

Place the onion, celery, garlic, peas and stock in a non-stick saucepan over a medium heat and bring to the boil. Reduce the heat to medium and cook for 20 minutes.

Using a stick blender or food processor, blend the soup with the chopped mint until smooth. Remove from the heat and serve immediately, drizzled with the yogurt and a sprinkling of black pepper.

Syns per serving F F 5½

900ml vegetable stock

225g new potatoes, diced

225g baby carrots, diced

175g baby broad beans, shelled

4 ripe tomatoes, skinned and chopped

400g can cannellini beans, drained

110g dried short-shaped pasta

2 level tbsp red pesto sauce

pistou soup

serves 4 Ⓥ

takes 30 minutes

Place the stock in a large saucepan with the potatoes, carrots and beans, cover and simmer for 10 minutes.

Add the tomatoes to the soup along with the cannellini beans and the pasta. Continue cooking, uncovered, for a further 12 minutes until the pasta is al dente.

Remove from the heat, stir in the pesto sauce and serve immediately.

Syns per serving 1½ 1½ 12

1 large onion, peeled and chopped

1 leek, trimmed and chopped

2 celery sticks, chopped

2 garlic cloves, peeled and crushed

1 litre hot vegetable stock

225g tomatoes, skinned and chopped

450g green cabbage, shredded

60g dried pasta shapes

225g canned cannellini beans, drained

salt and freshly ground black pepper

chopped fresh flat-leaf parsley, to serve

tuscan ribollita

serves 4

takes 35-40 minutes

Place the onion, leek, celery, garlic and 300ml of the stock in a large heavy-based saucepan. Cover the pan, bring to the boil and simmer for 5-10 minutes.

Add the tomatoes and cabbage to the pan along with the remaining stock, pasta shapes and cannellini beans.

Bring back to the boil and simmer for about 20 minutes, until the pasta is cooked and the vegetables are tender. Season and serve sprinkled with chopped parsley.

Syns per serving

2 onions, peeled and
finely chopped

2 garlic cloves, peeled
and finely chopped

1 large potato, peeled
and cut into 1.5cm dice

200g watercress, finely
chopped

1 litre vegetable stock

6 tbsp finely chopped
fresh parsley

salt and freshly ground
black pepper

fat free natural fromage
frais and watercress
sprigs, to serve

watercress
soup

serves 4 ❄ Ⓥ
takes 25-30 minutes

Place the onions, garlic, potato, watercress, stock and
parsley in a non-stick saucepan over a medium heat
and bring to the boil. Cover and cook gently for
10-12 minutes, or until the potatoes are tender.

Using a stick blender or food processor, blend the
soup until smooth. Season to taste and serve the soup
with a swirl of fromage frais and a sprig of watercress.

Syns per serving Ⓕ Ⓕ 1½

2cm piece root ginger, peeled and cut into very thin matchsticks

1 garlic clove, peeled and crushed

600ml vegetable stock

100g pak choi or Chinese cabbage, finely shredded

75g carrots, peeled and cut into thin matchsticks

6 spring onions, trimmed and cut into thin diagonal slices

60g shiitake mushrooms, finely sliced

100g tofu (plain/naturally smoked), drained and cut into 2.5cm cubes

2 tbsp dark soy sauce

freshly ground black pepper

chinese mushroom & tofu soup

serves 4

takes 20 minutes

Place the ginger, garlic and stock in a large saucepan and bring to the boil. Reduce the heat and simmer for 3-4 minutes.

Add the vegetables and tofu to the stock, bring back to the boil, lower the heat and simmer for 2 minutes. Add the soy sauce and black pepper to taste and serve immediately.

Try replacing the carrots with strips of cucumber, and use chestnut or oyster mushrooms in place of the shiitake.

Syns per serving F F F

for the dumplings

2 spring onions, trimmed and finely chopped

225g extra lean turkey breast mince

1 tsp dried mixed herbs

salt and freshly ground black pepper

for the broth

1 large onion, peeled and roughly chopped

2 celery sticks, thinly sliced

350g swede, peeled and diced

2 medium carrots, peeled and cut into bite-sized chunks

1.2 litres chicken stock

low calorie cooking spray

a small handful chopped fresh flat-leaf parsley

turkey dumplings
in vegetable broth

serves 4

takes 35 minutes plus chilling

First, make the dumplings. In a large bowl mix together the spring onions, turkey mince, dried herbs and plenty of seasoning. Mix well to combine and then divide into 20 portions. Form into small balls and place on a plate. Cover and chill for 30 minutes.

Meanwhile, place the onion, celery, swede, carrots and stock into a saucepan and bring to the boil. Cover and simmer for 15 minutes until the carrots and swede are tender.

As the soup is cooking, spray a large frying pan with low calorie cooking spray and add the dumplings. Cook for 8-10 minutes over a medium heat, shaking the pan frequently, until the dumplings are golden and cooked through. Add to the soup. Season to taste and serve scattered with the chopped parsley.

Syns per serving

nice & spicy

Inspired by flavours from Vietnam to Mexico, this tongue-tingling selection of soups will take you around the world in 16 bowls!

curried parsnip & apple soup

1 large onion, peeled and finely chopped

2 garlic cloves, peeled and crushed

500g parsnips, peeled and diced

1 litre hot vegetable stock

2 tsp curry powder

1 tsp ground ginger

1 tsp dried thyme

2 level tbsp apple sauce

150g fat free natural yogurt, plus extra to serve

salt and freshly ground black pepper

1 tbsp chopped fresh flat-leaf parsley

serves 4 **V**

takes 40 minutes

Place the onion, garlic and parsnips in a large, heavy-based saucepan along with 250ml of the stock. Cover the pan and bring to the boil.

Boil for 5-10 minutes then add the curry powder, ground ginger, thyme and remaining stock to the pan. Bring back to the boil then cover the pan and simmer for 15-20 minutes.

Purée the soup in a blender or food processor, then return it to the pan and add the apple sauce and yogurt. Reheat, stirring, over the lowest possible heat, taking care not to let it boil.

Season to taste and serve sprinkled with parsley and a swirl of yogurt.

Syns per serving ½ ½ 4½

indian
green pea soup

1 large onion, peeled
and chopped

2 garlic cloves, peeled
and crushed

110g potatoes, peeled
and cut into small dice

2cm piece root ginger,
peeled and finely chopped

2 tsp ground cumin

1.5 litres hot
vegetable stock

1 chilli, deseeded
and chopped

½ level tsp crushed
coriander seeds

275g frozen peas

salt and freshly ground
black pepper

juice of ½ lime

150g fat free natural yogurt,
plus extra to serve

paprika, to garnish

serves 4 **V**

takes 35-40 minutes

Place the onion, garlic, potatoes, ginger, cumin and
300ml of the stock in a large heavy-based saucepan.
Cover the pan, bring to the boil and simmer for
10 minutes.

Add the chopped chilli and coriander seeds to the
saucepan, together with the remaining stock and
the peas. Bring to the boil, then reduce the heat and
simmer for 10-15 minutes, until the vegetables are
tender. Season to taste and add the lime juice.

Purée in a blender or food processor, return to the pan
and stir in the yogurt. Heat through over a very low
heat without letting it boil. Serve hot, sprinkled with
paprika and a swirl of yogurt.

Syns per serving **F** **F** **3½**

350g cooked skinless and boneless chicken, shredded

1 bunch spring onions, trimmed and chopped

1.5cm piece root ginger, peeled and grated

110g small shiitake or button mushrooms, sliced

2 tbsp dark soy sauce

2 tbsp dry sherry

2 level tsp light brown sugar

1.2 litres chicken stock

100g carrots, peeled and sliced

175g baby sweetcorn, trimmed and sliced

chinese chicken & mushroom soup

serves 4 ❄

takes 20-25 minutes

Place the chicken in a bowl and stir in the spring onions, reserving a few to garnish. Add the ginger, mushrooms, soy sauce, sherry and sugar, mix well and set aside.

Pour the stock into a large saucepan and bring to the boil. Add the carrots and baby sweetcorn and simmer for 1 minute. Stir in the chicken mixture, bring back to the boil and simmer for 10 minutes.

Serve the soup garnished with the reserved spring onions.

Syns per serving ♥1 ♥8½ ♥1

low calorie cooking spray

1 onion, peeled and
finely chopped

6 green cardamom pods

2 fat red chillies,
finely chopped

2cm piece root ginger,
peeled and finely
chopped or crushed

2 garlic cloves, peeled
and crushed

1 tbsp Madras curry
powder

450g lean beef fillet, all
visible fat removed, cut
into bite-sized chunks

2 tsp ground coriander

1 tsp ground cumin

500ml beef stock

salt and freshly ground
black pepper

400g can chopped
tomatoes

4 tbsp fat free
natural yogurt

2 ripe tomatoes,
cut into thin wedges

fresh coriander sprigs,
to serve

spicy
beef soup

serves 4

takes 1 hour 45 minutes

Spray a large saucepan with low calorie cooking spray
and heat gently. Add the onion and cardamom pods
and cook for 3-4 minutes until the onion is beginning
to soften. Stir in the fresh chillies, ginger and garlic and
cook for 2 minutes, stirring continuously.

Add the curry powder and beef to the saucepan and
cook, stirring occasionally, for 2-3 minutes until the
meat is sealed. Add the ground coriander, cumin and
stock and bring to the boil. Season, cover tightly and
reduce the heat to low. Cook gently for 1½ hours,
stirring occasionally, until the meat is tender. Remove
the cardamon pods – they should be floating on top of
the sauce.

Add the canned tomatoes and heat through gently.

To serve, spoon into shallow soup bowls. Drizzle with
the yogurt, scatter over the tomato wedges and fresh
coriander and serve immediately.

This soup is delicious served with strips of wholemeal
pitta bread.

Syns per serving F 7½ F

low calorie cooking spray

1 large onion, peeled and roughly chopped

2 tsp nigella (black onion) seeds

2 garlic cloves, peeled and minced

1 fat red chilli, deseeded and cut into thin strips, plus sliced red chilli to garnish (optional)

½ tsp turmeric

2 tbsp medium curry powder

750g potatoes, peeled and cut into bite-sized chunks

750ml vegetable stock

100g shredded spring greens or cabbage

4 tbsp fat free natural yogurt, plus extra to garnish

salt and freshly ground black pepper

goan potato soup

serves 4 ❄ Ⓥ

takes 35 minutes

Add a spritz of low calorie cooking spray to a large saucepan, add the onion, nigella seeds, garlic, chilli, turmeric, curry powder and 150ml of water and cook for 2-3 minutes.

Stir in the potatoes and vegetable stock. Bring to the boil, cover and simmer for 15 minutes or until the potatoes are just tender.

Stir the shredded greens into the soup and simmer for 3 minutes. Stir in the yogurt and season to taste before serving.

For extra 'zing' sprinkle with sliced red chilli and an extra swirl of yogurt.

Syns per serving Ⓕ Ⓕ ❼

low calorie cooking spray

350g lean lamb leg steaks, all visible fat removed, cut into small chunks

1 large onion, peeled and finely chopped

2 garlic cloves, peeled and crushed

4cm piece root ginger, peeled and crushed

3 tbsp medium curry powder

400g can chopped tomatoes

1 tsp sweetener

750ml lamb stock

2 large carrots, peeled and finely chopped

110g baby leaf spinach

salt and freshly ground black pepper

curried lamb soup

serves 4

takes 1 hour 10 minutes

Spray a large, heavy-based casserole dish with low calorie cooking spray and cook the lamb, onion, garlic, ginger and curry powder for 5-6 minutes, stirring occasionally, until the lamb is browned.

Add the tomatoes, sweetener and stock and bring to the boil. Lower the heat, then cover and simmer gently for 30-35 minutes, stirring often, or until the meat is tender.

Stir in the carrots and cook for a further 20 minutes, or until just tender. Stir in the spinach until wilted. Season to taste before serving.

Syns per serving F 7 F

1 tbsp cumin seeds

low calorie cooking spray

1 bunch spring onions,
trimmed and roughly
chopped

2 carrots, peeled and
finely chopped

1 large red pepper,
deseeded and
finely chopped

2 garlic cloves, peeled
and crushed

2 tbsp harissa paste

2 tsp ground coriander

1.5 litres vegetable stock

400g can chopped
tomatoes

1 large baking potato,
peeled and diced

400g can chickpeas,
drained and rinsed

salt and freshly ground
black pepper

chopped fresh coriander,
to serve

moroccan
chickpea soup

serves 4

takes 40 minutes

Tip the cumin seeds into a dry frying pan and cook
over a low heat for 20-30 seconds until fragrant, then
crush lightly and set aside.

Spray a large saucepan with low calorie cooking spray
and heat gently. Add the spring onions, reserving a few
to garnish, and cook for 2-3 minutes. Stir in the carrots,
pepper and garlic and cook for 2-3 minutes, stirring
occasionally.

Add the crushed cumin seeds, harissa paste and
ground coriander and cook, stirring, for 1 minute.
Pour over the stock and chopped tomatoes and
scatter over the potato. Bring to the boil and simmer
for 15-20 minutes until the carrots and potatoes
are tender.

Stir in the chickpeas and cook until warmed through.
Season to taste and serve scattered with fresh coriander
and the reserved spring onions.

Syns per serving ½ ½ 6

2 red peppers, deseeded and chopped

1 red chilli, deseeded and chopped

1 large onion, peeled and chopped

2 carrots, peeled and finely chopped

low calorie cooking spray

900ml vegetable stock

1 level tbsp tomato purée

500g carton passata

salt and freshly ground black pepper

a handful of rocket leaves, to serve

for the horseradish sauce

4 tbsp quark

2 tbsp skimmed milk

2 level tsp creamed horseradish

red pepper soup
with horseradish

serves 4

takes 45 minutes

Preheat the oven to 200°C/Fan 180°C/Gas 6.

Place the peppers, chilli, onion and carrots in a roasting tin, spray with low calorie cooking spray and roast for 35 minutes or until tender.

Place the roasting tin over a low heat on the hob and pour over the stock, tomato purée and passata. Bring to the boil, scraping up any pan juices, then allow to cool a little. Transfer to a food processor, season well and blend until smooth.

To make the horseradish sauce mix together the quark, milk and creamed horseradish. Serve the soup topped with a spoonful of horseradish sauce, more freshly ground black pepper and a few rocket leaves.

Syns per serving

1 large onion, peeled and chopped

1 leek, trimmed and chopped

2 garlic cloves, peeled and crushed

1 carrot, peeled and diced

1 red chilli, deseeded and chopped

1.5 litres vegetable stock

400g cooked black beans

1 level tbsp tomato purée

1 tsp ground cumin

1 tsp crushed coriander seeds

salt and freshly ground black pepper

fat free natural fromage frais, chopped fresh coriander and a sprinkle of smoked paprika, to garnish

mexican black bean soup

serves 4 ❄ 🅥

takes 45 minutes

Place the onion, leek, garlic, carrot and chilli in a large heavy-based saucepan with 300ml of the stock. Cover the pan and bring to the boil.

Boil for 10 minutes then add the remaining stock and half of the black beans and bring back to the boil. Reduce the heat, and stir in the tomato purée, cumin and crushed coriander seeds. Simmer gently for 20-25 minutes.

Purée the soup in a blender or food processor and return to the pan. Add the remaining black beans, season to taste and reheat gently.

Serve hot topped with a spoonful of fromage frais and sprinkled with coriander and smoked paprika.

Syns per serving   5

thai green chicken soup

2 large skinless and boneless chicken breasts

4 kaffir lime leaves, finely shredded

2 tbsp trimmed and very finely chopped lemon grass

2cm piece root ginger, peeled and crushed

1.2 litres chicken stock

juice of 1 lime

6 tbsp very finely chopped fresh coriander

2 tsp nam pla (Thai fish sauce)

1 red chilli, deseeded and very finely sliced

4 tbsp light coconut milk

4 spring onions, trimmed and finely shredded

200g sugar snap peas, trimmed

salt and freshly ground black pepper

1 red chilli, deseeded and finely sliced, to serve (optional)

serves 4 ❄

takes 45 minutes

Place the chicken, kaffir lime leaves, lemon grass, ginger and stock in a medium saucepan and bring to the boil.

Reduce the heat to low, cover and simmer gently for 20-25 minutes or until the chicken is cooked through. Remove the chicken with a slotted spoon and, when cool enough to handle, tear into bite-sized shreds.

Return the chicken to the pan and add the lime juice, chopped coriander, nam pla, red chilli, coconut milk, most of the spring onions and the sugar snap peas. Season well and heat gently for 4-5 minutes until warmed through.

Serve immediately, garnished with the remaining spring onions and red chilli, if using.

If you can't find kaffir lime leaves use the juice of two limes instead and if you can't find nam pla use light soy sauce instead.

Syns per serving   1 5 1

1.2 litres fish stock

4 kaffir lime leaves

2cm piece root ginger, peeled and finely grated

1 red chilli, deseeded and finely sliced

1 tbsp trimmed and finely chopped lemon grass

300g button mushrooms, quartered

250g baby leaf spinach

300g cooked and peeled tiger prawns (with or without tails)

juice of 1 lemon

salt and freshly ground black pepper

hot & sour
seafood soup

serves 4

takes 20 minutes

Place the stock, kaffir lime leaves, ginger, red chilli and lemon grass into a saucepan and bring to the boil. Add the mushrooms, reduce the heat to a gentle simmer and cook for 2-3 minutes.

Add the spinach and prawns and simmer for a further 2-3 minutes until heated through.

Remove from the heat, add the lemon juice, season to taste and serve immediately.

If you can't find kaffir lime leaves use the juice of two limes instead.

Syns per serving

low calorie cooking spray

1 onion, peeled and
finely grated

6cm piece root ginger,
peeled and crushed

3 garlic cloves,
peeled and crushed

1 tbsp ground coriander

1 tbsp ground cumin

1 tsp turmeric

400g can chopped
tomatoes

2 tsp korma curry powder

750ml chicken stock

650g fresh mussels,
scrubbed

1 small leek, trimmed
and very thinly sliced

salt and freshly ground
black pepper

4 tbsp fat free natural
fromage frais

curried
mussel soup

serves 4

takes 50 minutes

Spray a large frying pan with low calorie cooking spray
and heat gently. Add the onion and cook for 3 minutes
until softened. Stir in the ginger and garlic and simmer
for 1-2 minutes.

Add the ground coriander, cumin, turmeric, tomatoes
and korma curry powder and cook for 2-3 minutes,
stirring continuously.

Pour over the stock. Bring to the boil, cover, reduce
the heat to low and allow to simmer very gently for
20 minutes, stirring occasionally.

Meanwhile, clean the mussels thoroughly under cold
running water, removing any beards and discarding
any mussels that are already open or cracked. Add the
mussels and leek to the soup and cook for 6-8 minutes
until the mussels have opened. Discard any that remain
closed. Season to taste, stir in the fromage frais and
serve immediately.

Syns per serving F 2½ F

110g no-soak red lentils

low calorie cooking spray

1 large onion, peeled
and roughly chopped

1 large garlic clove,
peeled and crushed

2cm piece root ginger,
peeled and crushed

2 tbsp tikka masala
curry powder

450g sweet potatoes,
peeled and finely diced

450g swede, peeled
and finely diced

400g can chopped
tomatoes

1.2 litres vegetable stock

salt and freshly ground
black pepper

a small handful chopped
fresh mint, to serve

spiced red lentil
dhal soup

serves 4 Ⓥ

takes 30-35 minutes

Cook the lentils in boiling water for 12-15 minutes, drain
and set aside.

Meanwhile, spray a large saucepan with low calorie
cooking spray, add the onion and cook for
3-4 minutes. Add the garlic, ginger, curry powder,
sweet potatoes, swede and tomatoes. Stir well, cover
and cook over a low heat for 5-6 minutes.

Add the stock and lentils, stir well and simmer for a
further 10-12 minutes. Season to taste and serve
scattered with chopped mint.

Syns per serving   9½

low calorie cooking spray

1 lemon grass stalk, trimmed and very finely sliced

1 garlic clove, peeled and crushed

2cm piece root ginger, peeled and crushed

1 red chilli, deseeded and thinly sliced

850ml vegetable stock

1 large carrot, peeled, halved and cut into thin matchsticks

110g baby sweetcorn, halved

200g raw peeled tiger prawns

4 spring onions, trimmed and thinly sliced

100g bean sprouts, rinsed

1 tbsp nam pla (Thai fish sauce)

1 tbsp light soy sauce

juice of 1 lime

asian prawn
& vegetable soup

serves 4

takes 25 minutes

Spray a large saucepan with low calorie cooking spray. Add the lemon grass, garlic, ginger and chilli and cook for 1-2 minutes. Add the stock, carrot and baby sweetcorn, bring to the boil, then reduce the heat, cover and simmer very gently for 6-8 minutes.

Stir in the prawns and cook for 1-2 minutes until they turn pink. Add the spring onions, bean sprouts, nam pla, soy sauce and lime juice and simmer gently for no longer than 2 minutes until warmed through (do not boil). Serve straight away.

Syns per serving F 2 F

1 tsp sunflower oil

1 tsp Szechuan peppercorns, roughly crushed

1 lemon grass stalk, trimmed and sliced

1 cinnamon stick, broken into pieces

2 star anise

4cm piece root ginger, peeled and sliced

1.5 litres beef stock

1 tbsp nam pla (Thai fish sauce)

juice of 1 lime

100g dried fine rice noodles

250g very lean rump or frying steak, thinly sliced

100g bean sprouts, rinsed

1 large red chilli, finely chopped

4 spring onions, trimmed and thinly sliced, plus shredded spring onions to garnish

lime wedges, to serve (optional)

vietnamese beef pho

serves 4 ❄

takes 1 hour

Heat the oil in a saucepan, add the peppercorns, lemon grass, cinnamon, star anise and ginger and cook for 1 minute to release their flavours. Add the stock and bring to the boil, stirring. Reduce the heat, cover and simmer gently for 40 minutes.

Strain the mixture, discarding the spices, and then return the liquid to the pan and stir in the nam pla and lime juice.

Cook the noodles in a pan of boiling water as directed on the packet then drain and divide between four bowls.

Add the steak and bean sprouts to the soup and cook for 1-2 minutes. Divide the chilli and sliced spring onions between the bowls and then ladle the soup on top. Garnish with shredded spring onions and serve with lime wedges for extra zing.

Syns per serving   ½ 4½ 5

mulligatawny

1 small onion, peeled and chopped

2 celery sticks, trimmed and chopped

1 carrot, peeled and diced

2 tsp mild curry powder

500ml chicken stock

100g dried basmati rice

400g can chopped tomatoes

2 large skinless and boneless chicken breasts, diced

salt and freshly ground black pepper

4 tbsp chopped fresh coriander

serves 4

takes 1 hour

Place the onion, celery, carrot, curry powder, stock, rice and tomatoes in a large saucepan and bring to the boil.

Reduce the heat to low, cover and simmer gently for 30 minutes.

Add the chicken and coriander and season well. Cook for 8-10 minutes or until the chicken is cooked through then remove from the heat. Scatter the coriander and serve straight away.

Syns per serving F 4 4½

a meal in a bowl

Get your big bowl ready! Bursting with Free and Superfree Foods, these hearty soups are packed with flavour *and* filling power!

low calorie cooking spray

6 medium onions,
peeled and thinly sliced

1 garlic clove, peeled
and thinly sliced

1 tbsp fresh thyme
leaves, plus thyme sprigs
to garnish

1 litre vegetable stock

salt and freshly ground
black pepper

french onion soup

serves 4 ❄ Ⓥ

takes 50-55 minutes

Spray a heavy-based saucepan with low calorie
cooking spray. Add the onions and garlic and sauté for
20-25 minutes over a very low heat, until golden brown.

Stir well before adding the thyme and stock, bring to the
boil and simmer for about 10 minutes. Season the soup,
garnish with thyme sprigs and serve immediately.

Syns per serving Ⓕ Ⓕ Ⓕ

scotch broth

110g raw pearl barley

low calorie cooking spray

1 onion, peeled and finely chopped

2 carrots, peeled and finely chopped

2 celery sticks, finely chopped

1 garlic clove, peeled and crushed

400g can chopped tomatoes

1.2 litres vegetable stock

200g green cabbage, finely shredded

110g frozen peas

3 tbsp chopped fresh flat-leaf parsley

salt and freshly ground black pepper

serves 4 ❄ 🅥

takes 1 hour

Place the pearl barley in a pan of rapidly boiling water and cook for 25 minutes. Drain and set aside.

Meanwhile, spray a pan with low calorie cooking spray and place over a medium heat. Add the onion, carrots, celery and garlic and stir-fry for 3-4 minutes. Add the tomatoes and stock and bring to the boil. Reduce the heat and simmer for 15-20 minutes.

Add the cabbage to the pan along with the peas and the pearl barley. Gently cook for 15-20 minutes, stirring occasionally. Stir in the parsley and season well before serving.

Syns per serving   6

rustic bean & pasta soup

2 onions, peeled and finely chopped

2 garlic cloves, peeled and crushed

3 celery sticks, trimmed and cut into 1.5cm lengths

2 carrots, peeled and diced

400g can chopped tomatoes

900ml vegetable stock

60g dried soup pasta

400g can mixed beans, drained and rinsed

4 tbsp chopped fresh flat-leaf parsley

salt and freshly ground black pepper

serves 4 ❄ Ⓥ
takes 45 minutes

Place the onions, garlic, celery, carrots, tomatoes and stock in a large pan. Bring to the boil, reduce the heat and simmer for 15-20 minutes.

Stir in the pasta and cook for a further 8-10 minutes or until just tender. Add the beans and heat through.

Stir in the parsley, season to taste and serve.

This soup is also delicious served cold on a hot summer's day. The flavour improves if you make it a day or two ahead and store it in the fridge.

Syns per serving

1 medium onion, peeled and finely chopped

1 garlic clove, peeled and finely chopped

1 tsp dried oregano

300ml vegetable stock

1 large green pepper, deseeded and cut into small chunks

400g can mixed pulses, drained and rinsed

600ml passata

1 large courgette, trimmed and diced

325g can sweetcorn kernels, drained

salt and freshly ground black pepper

chopped fresh flat-leaf parsley, to garnish

hearty bean & vegetable soup

serves 4

takes 40 minutes

Place the onion and garlic in a large saucepan along with the dried oregano and half of the stock. Bring to the boil, cover and simmer for 5 minutes.

Stir the green pepper, pulses and passata into the onion mixture along with the remaining stock. Bring to the boil, cover and simmer for 10 minutes.

Add the courgette and sweetcorn, stir well and simmer for a further 10 minutes. Season to taste and scatter over the parsley before serving.

Syns per serving F F 5½

1 onion, peeled
and finely chopped

1 medium potato, peeled
and finely chopped

800ml vegetable stock

400g frozen peas

2 tbsp finely chopped
fresh tarragon, plus
tarragon sprigs to garnish

200g premium lean ham,
cut into small dice

salt and freshly ground
black pepper

pea & ham soup

serves 4

takes 40 minutes

Place the onion, potato, stock and peas in a large
saucepan. Bring to the boil then reduce the heat and
simmer gently for 20 minutes or until the potatoes are
tender.

Stir in the tarragon and, using a stick blender, process
the soup until smooth.

Stir in the ham, reserving some to garnish, and bring
back to the boil.

Season to taste and sprinkle with the remaining ham
and the tarragon sprigs before serving.

Syns per serving F 3½ 5

1 small butternut squash, halved, deseeded and each half cut into four pieces

1 red pepper, halved, deseeded and each half cut into four pieces

1 yellow pepper, halved, deseeded and each half cut into four pieces

1 large red onion, peeled and cut into thick wedges

2 large beefsteak tomatoes, halved

a few fresh rosemary sprigs

2 garlic cloves, peeled and thinly sliced

juice of 1 lemon

salt and freshly ground black pepper

low calorie cooking spray

1.2 litres vegetable stock

fresh thyme sprigs, to garnish

roast mediterranean vegetable soup

serves 4 ❄ Ⓥ

takes 50 minutes

Preheat the oven to 200°C/Fan 180°C/Gas 6.

Arrange all the vegetables and rosemary sprigs on a large non-stick baking sheet or in a shallow roasting tin. Sprinkle over the garlic and lemon juice. Season well, spray with low calorie cooking spray and bake in the oven for 30 minutes or until tender.

Discard the rosemary. Scoop out the flesh from the squash and place in a food processor or blender. Reserving a piece of each pepper and red onion to garnish, add all the other vegetables and 450ml of the stock, and process for a few seconds until smooth.

Transfer to a large saucepan and stir in the remaining stock. Heat through for 4-5 minutes until piping hot and season to taste.

Slice the reserved pepper and onion pieces and place on top of the soup along with some thyme sprigs before serving.

Syns per serving Ⓕ Ⓕ Ⓕ

300g dried split red lentils

low calorie cooking spray

2 onions, peeled
and finely chopped

3 carrots, peeled
and finely chopped

4 celery sticks, trimmed
and finely chopped

2 garlic cloves, peeled
and finely diced

1 bay leaf

3 fresh parsley sprigs,
plus chopped fresh
flat-leaf parsley to garnish

1.5 litres vegetable stock

salt and freshly ground
black pepper

4 tbsp fat free natural
fromage frais, to serve

paprika, to garnish

lentil
broth

serves 4

takes 1 hour 10 minutes plus soaking

Wash the lentils in a sieve under cold running water.
Tip into a bowl and cover with hot water. Leave to soak
for 30 minutes.

Spray a large non-stick saucepan with low calorie
cooking spray and place over a medium heat. Add
the onions, carrots, celery and garlic and stir-fry for
10 minutes until softened.

Drain the lentils and add to the pan with the bay leaf,
parsley sprigs and the stock. Bring to the boil, reduce
the heat and simmer gently for 30 minutes, skimming
off any scum that comes to the surface.

Remove the bay leaf and parsley sprigs, transfer the
mixture to a food processor and blend until smooth.

Return the soup to the pan, season well and reheat.
Serve with a swirl of fromage frais and a sprinkling of
chopped parsley and paprika.

Syns per serving F F 12

1 large onion, peeled and finely chopped

1 celery stick, finely chopped

2 bay leaves

1.2 litres vegetable stock

1 large potato, peeled and diced

2 large carrots, peeled and finely chopped

225g pack cooked beetroot in juice, drained and finely diced

salt and freshly ground black pepper

fat free natural fromage frais and chopped fresh flat-leaf parsley, to serve

mixed root vegetable soup

serves 4 ❄ Ⓥ

takes 55 minutes

Place the onion and celery in a large saucepan with the bay leaves and 150ml of the stock. Bring to the boil, cover and simmer for 5 minutes until tender.

Add the potato, carrots and remaining stock. Bring back to the boil, cover and simmer for 25 minutes until tender.

Add the beetroot and simmer for a further 5 minutes. Discard the bay leaves.

Transfer to a blender or food processor and process for a few seconds until smooth. Season to taste.

Reheat the soup, if necessary, before serving topped with a little fromage frais and chopped parsley.

Syns per serving

low calorie cooking spray

1 onion, peeled
and finely chopped

2 garlic cloves,
peeled and crushed

2cm piece root ginger,
peeled and finely grated

2 celery sticks, finely
chopped

1 large potato, peeled
and cut into 1.5cm dice

1 large carrot, peeled
and cut into 1.5cm dice

600ml boiling hot
vegetable stock

1 tbsp mild curry powder

125g dried red lentils,
rinsed and drained

600ml passata

salt and freshly ground
black pepper

chopped fresh coriander,
to garnish

tomato, lentil
& vegetable soup

serves 4

takes 30 minutes

Spray a large saucepan with low calorie cooking spray
and place over a high heat. Add the onion, garlic, ginger,
celery, potato and carrot and stir-fry for 1-2 minutes.

Add the remaining ingredients, except the seasoning,
and bring to the boil. Cover and simmer gently for
15-20 minutes or until the lentils are cooked. Season
well and serve sprinkled with coriander.

Syns per serving F F 6½

325g can sweetcorn kernels, drained

low calorie cooking spray

1 large onion, peeled and finely chopped

3 garlic cloves, peeled and crushed

1 tsp ground cumin

1 tsp ground coriander

300ml skimmed milk

500ml vegetable stock

200g potatoes, peeled and cut into 1.5cm dice

1 red pepper, deseeded and cut into 1.5cm dice

salt and freshly ground black pepper

2 tbsp fat free natural fromage frais

3 tbsp chopped fresh coriander

corn & coriander chowder

serves 4 **ⓥ**

takes 25 minutes

Put half of the sweetcorn in a food processor and blend to a purée. Set aside.

Spray a large saucepan with low calorie cooking spray and place over a low heat. Add the onion and garlic and cook for 4-5 minutes.

Stir in the ground cumin, coriander, the puréed and the whole sweetcorn, milk, stock, potatoes and red pepper. Bring to the boil, reduce the heat and simmer for 10 minutes or until the potatoes are tender. Season to taste.

Remove from the heat and stir in the fromage frais and chopped coriander. Serve immediately.

Syns per serving 1½ 1½ 6

1 onion, peeled and finely chopped

1 carrot, peeled and diced

2 celery sticks, chopped

1 garlic clove, peeled and crushed

1 large potato, peeled and diced

60g dried pasta

1 litre vegetable stock

400g can chopped tomatoes

400g can cannellini beans, drained

60g savoy cabbage leaves, cut into strips

a handful of fresh basil leaves, finely chopped

salt and freshly ground black pepper

minestrone soup

serves 4 ⓥ
takes 40 minutes

Place the onion, carrot, celery, garlic and potato in a large pan, along with the pasta and stock. Bring to the boil, reduce the heat, cover and simmer for 15 minutes or until the vegetables are tender.

Stir in the tomatoes and beans and simmer for 5 minutes. Add the cabbage and basil and cook until the cabbage starts to wilt. Season to taste before serving.

Syns per serving Ⓕ Ⓕ ⑦

low calorie cooking spray

1 onion, peeled
and finely chopped

2 celery sticks, finely
chopped

2 garlic cloves, peeled
and finely chopped

1 litre vegetable stock

4 ripe tomatoes, deseeded
and finely chopped

200g cooked brown or
white basmati rice

400g frozen peas

salt and freshly ground
black pepper

fresh chives, to garnish

tomato, rice & pea soup

serves 4 🥶 🅥

takes 20 minutes

Spray a saucepan with low calorie cooking spray and place over a medium heat. Add the onion, celery and garlic and stir-fry for 2-3 minutes. Add the stock and tomatoes and bring to the boil.

Reduce the heat to medium and cook for 5-6 minutes. Add the rice and peas and season well. Bring back to the boil and cook for 3-4 minutes, until the vegetables are cooked through.

Remove from the heat and serve garnished with chives.

Syns per serving 🅕 🅕 7

for the pesto

4 tbsp fat free natural fromage frais

2 level tbsp freshly grated Parmesan cheese

1 garlic clove, peeled and crushed

a small bunch fresh basil, finely chopped

salt and freshly ground black pepper

for the soup

110g lean unsmoked rindless back bacon, all visible fat removed, finely chopped

1 large onion, peeled and finely chopped

1 large carrot, peeled and finely chopped

2 celery sticks, chopped

300ml vegetable stock

1 red pepper, deseeded and cut into small pieces

1 tsp dried oregano

2 x 400g cans chopped tomatoes with garlic

italian-style bacon soup

serves 4

takes 40 minutes

Mix all the pesto ingredients together and season to taste. Cover and chill until required.

To make the soup, place the bacon and onion in a large non-stick saucepan and heat gently until the bacon juices run. Cook for 2-3 minutes, until the onion starts to soften.

Stir the carrot and celery into the pan and pour over half of the stock. Bring to the boil, cover and simmer for 5 minutes.

Add the red pepper, oregano, tomatoes and remaining stock and season to taste. Bring to the boil and simmer for 15 minutes until thick and tender. Serve the soup topped with a spoonful of pesto.

Syns per serving ½ 2½ ½

1 onion, peeled and finely chopped

2 carrots, peeled and grated

2 lean back bacon rashers, all visible fat removed, finely chopped

2 large skinless and boneless chicken breasts, cut into thin strips

600g canned chopped tomatoes

400ml chicken stock

1 tbsp chopped rosemary

finely grated zest and juice of 1 lemon

salt and freshly ground black pepper

chopped fresh flat-leaf parsley, to garnish

italian chicken & tomato soup

serves 4

takes 25 minutes

Place the onion, carrots and bacon in a large non-stick saucepan and stir-fry for 2-3 minutes.

Add the chicken, tomatoes, stock, rosemary and lemon zest and juice. Bring to the boil, stir, then cover and simmer on a medium heat for 15 minutes, stirring occasionally. Season to taste and serve sprinkled with chopped parsley.

Syns per serving F 5 F

2 garlic cloves, peeled
and crushed

1 red onion, peeled
and finely chopped

2 tbsp red wine vinegar

2-3 tsp sweetener

400ml fish stock

400g can chopped
tomatoes with herbs

2 bay leaves

300g fresh mussels,
scrubbed

300g skinless firm white
fish (eg cod), cut into
bite-sized chunks

200g prepared squid rings

250g raw peeled tiger
prawns

salt and freshly ground
black pepper

3 tbsp chopped fresh
flat-leaf parsley

lemon wedges, to serve

chunky
fish soup

serves 4

takes 20 minutes

Put the garlic and onion in a large saucepan with the
vinegar and sweetener. Mix well and heat gently for
2-3 minutes. Add the stock, tomatoes and bay leaves,
bring to the boil, cover and simmer for 5-6 minutes.

Clean the mussels thoroughly under cold running
water, removing any beards and discarding any
mussels that are already open or cracked. Add the fish
and mussels to the pan and cook for 3-4 minutes.

Stir in the squid and prawns and continue to cook,
covered, for 2-3 minutes or until the squid is opaque and
the prawns have turned pink and are cooked through.

Remove from the heat, discarding the bay leaves and
any mussels that remain closed.

Season to taste and serve sprinkled with parsley and
the lemon wedges to squeeze over.

Syns per serving F 8½ F

seafood chowder

500g clams in shells

low calorie cooking spray

4 shallots, peeled and thinly sliced

4 garlic cloves, peeled and chopped

1 tbsp coriander seeds

1 tbsp fennel seeds

2 x 400g cans chopped tomatoes

1 tsp sweetener

a thick strip of orange peel

1 tbsp finely chopped fresh thyme

300ml fish stock

salt and freshly ground black pepper

700g skinless white fish fillets, cut into 4cm pieces

chopped fresh flat-leaf parsley, to garnish

serves 4

takes 55-60 minutes

Rinse the clams in cold water, discarding any that do not close when tapped firmly. Set aside.

Spray a heavy-based saucepan with low calorie cooking spray and place over a medium heat. Add the shallots, garlic, coriander and fennel seeds and stir-fry for 5-6 minutes.

Add the tomatoes, sweetener, orange peel, thyme and stock. Season well and bring to the boil. Lower the heat and simmer, uncovered, for 25-30 minutes, stirring occasionally.

Bring the chowder back to the boil and add the clams and fish. Cook for 4-5 minutes until all the clams have opened and the fish is cooked through. Discard any clams that remain closed.

Remove from the heat and garnish with chopped parsley before serving.

Syns per serving F 8½

cullen skink

low calorie cooking spray

1 onion, peeled and finely sliced

4 small leeks, trimmed and finely sliced

600g celeriac, peeled and cut into 2-3cm chunks

2 carrots, peeled and thickly sliced

600ml vegetable stock

1 bay leaf

freshly grated nutmeg

salt and freshly ground black pepper

400g undyed smoked haddock, skinned and cut into 5cm pieces

chopped fresh flat-leaf parsley, to garnish

serves 4 🌟

takes 1 hour 20 minutes

Spray a heavy-based pan with low calorie cooking spray. Add the onion and leeks and gently sweat them, covered, over a low heat for 15-20 minutes until they are extremely soft and almost sweet.

Add the celeriac, cover and cook gently for a further 10 minutes until starting to soften a little.

Add the carrots, stock, bay leaf and a little freshly grated nutmeg. Bring up to a simmer and season with some freshly ground black pepper.

Cook gently until the celeriac is very soft and beginning to break up – about 20-25 minutes. Then remove from the heat and, using the back of a fork, squash some of the celeriac into the soup mixture to thicken it.

Stir in the smoked haddock pieces, cover, and leave for 10 minutes to allow the haddock to just cook through in the heat of the stock.

Check the seasoning and serve garnished with chopped parsley.

Syns per serving 🅕 ④ 🅕

25g Flora Light margarine

1 large white onion,
peeled and chopped

25g plain flour

900ml chicken stock

1 leek, trimmed
and chopped

¼ cabbage, chopped

½ small cauliflower,
chopped

250g potatoes, peeled
and chopped

salt and freshly ground
black pepper

100ml skimmed milk

225g cooked skinless and
boneless chicken breast,
chopped

chopped fresh chives,
to garnish

chicken soup

serves 4

takes 50 minutes

Melt the margarine in a saucepan then stir in the onions. Add the flour and gradually pour in the stock.

Add the vegetables and simmer for 30 minutes until cooked through.

Place the soup in a blender or food processor and blend until smooth, then pass through a fine sieve.

Season to taste, then add the milk and chopped chicken.

Warm for 10 minutes to heat through and serve sprinkled with chives.

Syns per serving 3 8 5

low calorie cooking spray

1 large onion, peeled
and finely chopped

2 celery sticks, thinly sliced

2 garlic cloves, peeled
and finely chopped

1 litre vegetable stock

200g carrots, peeled
and sliced

200g potatoes, peeled
and diced

200g canned haricot beans,
rinsed and drained

1 ready-made
bouquet garni

salt and freshly ground
black pepper

chopped fresh chives,
to garnish

country vegetable soup

serves 4 ❄ Ⓥ

takes 30 minutes

Spray a non-stick saucepan with low calorie cooking spray and place over a medium heat. Add the onion, celery and garlic and stir-fry for 2-3 minutes.

Add the stock, carrots, potatoes, beans and the bouquet garni, bring to the boil and season well. Reduce the heat to medium and cook for 10-12 minutes.

Remove the bouquet garni and serve garnished with chives.

Syns per serving F F 4

rich & smooth

These heart-warming soups are super-colourful, super-smooth and bursting with Superfree vegetables!

borscht

450g uncooked beetroot, peeled and grated

1 large carrot, peeled and finely diced

1 onion, peeled and chopped

110g white cabbage, shredded

1 tsp sweetener

1 bay leaf

1.5 litres vegetable stock

salt and freshly ground black pepper

fat free natural fromage frais and chopped fresh chives, to garnish

serves 4
takes 4 hours 20 minutes

Preheat the oven to 140°C/Fan 120°C/Gas 1. Place all the ingredients in an ovenproof casserole dish, cover tightly and cook in the oven for 4 hours or until all the vegetables are tender. Remove the bay leaf and discard.

Transfer the vegetable mixture to a food processor and blend until smooth. Season to taste and blend again.

Ladle into bowls and garnish with a spoonful of fromage frais and some chopped chives before serving.

Syns per serving F F F

carrot & ginger soup

low calorie cooking spray

1 onion, peeled and chopped

2 celery sticks, chopped

2 garlic cloves, peeled and chopped

1.5cm piece root ginger, peeled and finely grated

1 litre vegetable stock

600g carrots, peeled and roughly chopped

salt and freshly ground black pepper

fat free natural yogurt and chopped fresh flat-leaf parsley, to garnish

serves 4 ✻ *V*
takes 35 minutes

Spray a pan with low calorie cooking spray and cook the onion, celery, garlic and ginger for 2-3 minutes. Add the stock and carrots and bring to the boil. Reduce the heat and simmer for 20 minutes, or until the carrots are tender. Season well.

Transfer the mixture to a blender or food processor and blend until almost smooth. Serve the soup with a swirl of yogurt and a sprinkling of parsley.

Syns per serving

6 large yellow peppers, halved and deseeded

10 ripe plum tomatoes, halved

6 garlic cloves, peeled

2 tbsp light soy sauce

2 tbsp roughly chopped fresh basil, plus fresh basil leaves to garnish

salt and freshly ground black pepper

roasted yellow pepper soup

serves 4

takes 1 hour

Preheat the oven to 200°C/Fan 180°C/Gas 6. Place the pepper halves on a non-stick baking sheet and roast for 15 minutes.

Add the tomatoes to the peppers with the garlic cloves and roast for a further 25-30 minutes.

Remove from the oven and carefully peel off and discard the skin from the peppers. Place the peeled peppers in a food processor with the tomatoes. Squeeze the garlic cloves from their skins into the processor along with the soy sauce and chopped basil. Add 300ml of hot water and process until smooth.

Transfer the mixture to a saucepan and place over a medium heat. Bring to the boil, remove from the heat and season well. Serve garnished with basil leaves.

Syns per serving Ⓕ Ⓕ Ⓕ

low calorie cooking spray

1 onion, peeled and chopped

1 medium butternut squash, peeled, deseeded and cut into wedges

1 small potato, peeled and quartered

2 garlic cloves, peeled and crushed

salt and freshly ground black pepper

900ml vegetable stock

thyme leaves, to serve

butternut squash soup

serves 4 ❄️ Ⓥ

takes 40 minutes

Spray a large pan with low calorie cooking spray and place over a low heat. Add the onion and cook for 1-2 minutes.

Add the butternut squash and potato and cook for 2 minutes over a medium heat. Add the garlic and season to taste. Pour in the stock and simmer for 25 minutes.

Using a stick blender or food processor, blend until smooth and serve sprinkled with thyme leaves.

Syns per serving 🅕 🅕 1

leek & potato soup

1 large onion, peeled and finely chopped

2 bay leaves

1.2 litres vegetable stock

700g potatoes, peeled and finely diced

1 large leek, trimmed and sliced, plus extra shredded and cooked leek to garnish (optional)

salt and freshly ground black pepper

150g fat free natural fromage frais

serves 4 Ⓥ

takes 45 minutes

Place the onion in a large saucepan with the bay leaves and 150ml of the stock. Bring to the boil, cover and simmer for 5 minutes.

Add the potatoes and leek to the pan. Pour in the remaining stock and season well. Bring to the boil, cover and simmer for 25 minutes until tender.

Discard the bay leaves and transfer the mixture to a food processor or blender. Blend until smooth and return to the saucepan.

Stir in the fromage frais and reheat the soup gently, without letting it boil. Season to taste and serve, garnished with shredded and cooked leek, if using.

Syns per serving Ⓕ Ⓕ ❤5

low calorie cooking spray

2 onions, peeled
and finely chopped

2 garlic cloves, peeled
and finely chopped

1 large potato, peeled
and cut into 1.5cm dice

500g button or chestnut
mushrooms, finely
chopped

1.5 litres vegetable stock

salt and freshly ground
black pepper

6 tbsp very finely
chopped fresh curly
parsley, plus extra
to serve

creamy mushroom soup

serves 4 ❄ *V*
takes 50 minutes

Spray a non-stick saucepan with low calorie cooking spray and place over a medium heat. Add the onions, garlic, potato and mushrooms and stir-fry over a high heat for 5-6 minutes.

Add the stock and bring to the boil. Cover and cook gently for 15-20 minutes or until the vegetables are tender. Season well.

Remove from the heat and stir in the parsley. Using a stick blender or food processor, blend the soup until smooth. Serve the soup sprinkled with parsley.

Try topping the soup with sliced mushrooms lightly fried in low calorie cooking spray.

Syns per serving F F 1½

cauliflower cheese soup

low calorie cooking spray

1 large onion, peeled and finely chopped

½ tsp smoked paprika

550g small cauliflower florets

800ml vegetable stock

10 The Laughing Cow Extra Light Cheese Triangles

salt and freshly ground black pepper

smoked paprika, to garnish

serves 4 Ⓥ

takes 25 minutes

Spray a large saucepan with low calorie cooking spray and heat gently. Add the onion and paprika and cook for 5 minutes, stirring occasionally, until softened slightly.

Add the cauliflower and stock and bring to the boil. Cover and simmer for 15 minutes until the cauliflower is just tender. Using a slotted spoon, lift out a few cauliflower florets and set aside to garnish. Stir the cheese triangles into the soup and blend with a stick blender or in a food processor until smooth. Season to taste.

To serve, spoon into shallow bowls and garnish with the cauliflower florets. Sprinkle with smoked paprika and serve immediately.

Syns per serving 2½ 2½ 2½

low calorie cooking spray

2 red onions, peeled
and finely chopped

3 garlic cloves, peeled
and crushed

15g fresh sage leaves

500g large potatoes,
peeled and diced

1.5 litres vegetable stock

250g baby leaf spinach,
plus extra leaves to
garnish

salt and freshly ground
black pepper

spinach, sage & potato soup

serves 4

takes 35 minutes

Spray a large saucepan with low calorie cooking spray and heat gently. Add the onions and cook for 2-3 minutes. Stir in the garlic and sage and 4 tablespoons of water and cook for 2-3 minutes or until the water has evaporated.

Add the potatoes and stock. Bring to the boil, cover and simmer for 15 minutes or until the potatoes are tender. Stir in the spinach and cook for 5 minutes or until wilted. Purée with a stick blender or whizz in batches in a food processor and season to taste.

Serve garnished with spinach leaves and a scattering of black pepper.

Syns per serving F F 5

700g sweet potatoes, peeled and cut into big chunks

6 large shallots, peeled and quartered

3 plump garlic cloves, unpeeled

1 carrot, peeled and cut into big chunks

1 tbsp harissa paste, plus extra to serve

1 tbsp olive oil

salt and freshly ground black pepper

1 litre hot vegetable stock

1 tsp runny honey

generous squeeze of lemon juice

fat free natural yogurt, to serve

moroccan roasted sweet potato soup

serves 4 ❄ Ⓥ

takes 1 hour 10 minutes

Preheat the oven to 200°/Fan 180°C/Gas 6. Put the sweet potatoes, shallots, garlic and carrot in a roasting tin. Mix the harissa with the oil, then pour over the vegetables and toss together so they are all well coated. Season and roast in the oven, turning occasionally, for 40 minutes or until tender and golden. Remove from the oven.

Squeeze the garlic cloves out of their skins into the roasting tin. Stir in the stock and honey, then scrape up all the bits from the bottom of the tin. Carefully transfer to a blender and whizz until smooth (you may need to do this in batches). Pour into a saucepan and reheat gently.

Add a good squeeze of lemon juice and season to taste with salt and freshly ground black pepper. Swirl the yogurt with a little harissa (½ Syn per level teaspoon) and top each bowl with a spoonful before serving.

Syns per serving 2 2 10

index

conversions

We have used metric measurements throughout this book. If you prefer to use imperial measurements, the following lists will help you.

grams/ounces	
15g	½oz
25g	1oz
60g	2½oz
75g	3oz
100g	3½oz
110g	4oz (¼lb)
125g	4½oz
150g	5oz
175g	6oz
200g	7oz
225g	8oz (½lb)
250g	9oz
275g	10oz
300g	11oz
350g	12oz (¾lb)
400g	14oz
450g	16oz (1lb)
500g	18oz (1lb 2oz)
550g	20oz (1¼lb)
600g	22oz (1lb 6oz)
650g	23oz (1lb 7oz)
700g	24oz (1lb 8oz)
750g	26oz (1lb 10oz)
800g	28oz (1lb 12oz)
900g	32oz (2lb)

millilitres/fluid ounces/pints	
100ml	3½fl oz
150ml	5fl oz (¼ pint)
200ml	7fl oz
250ml	9fl oz
300ml	11fl oz
350ml	12fl oz
400ml	14fl oz
450ml	16fl oz
500ml	18fl oz
600ml	20fl oz (1 pint)
750ml	26fl oz
800ml	28fl oz
850ml	30fl oz (1½ pints)
900ml	32fl oz
1 litre	35fl oz (1¾ pints)
1.2 litres	42fl oz (2 pints)
1.5 litres	54fl oz

centimetres/inches	
1.5cm	½ inch
2cm	¾ inch
2.5cm	1 inch
3cm	1¼ inches
4cm	1½ inches
5cm	2 inches
6cm	2½ inches